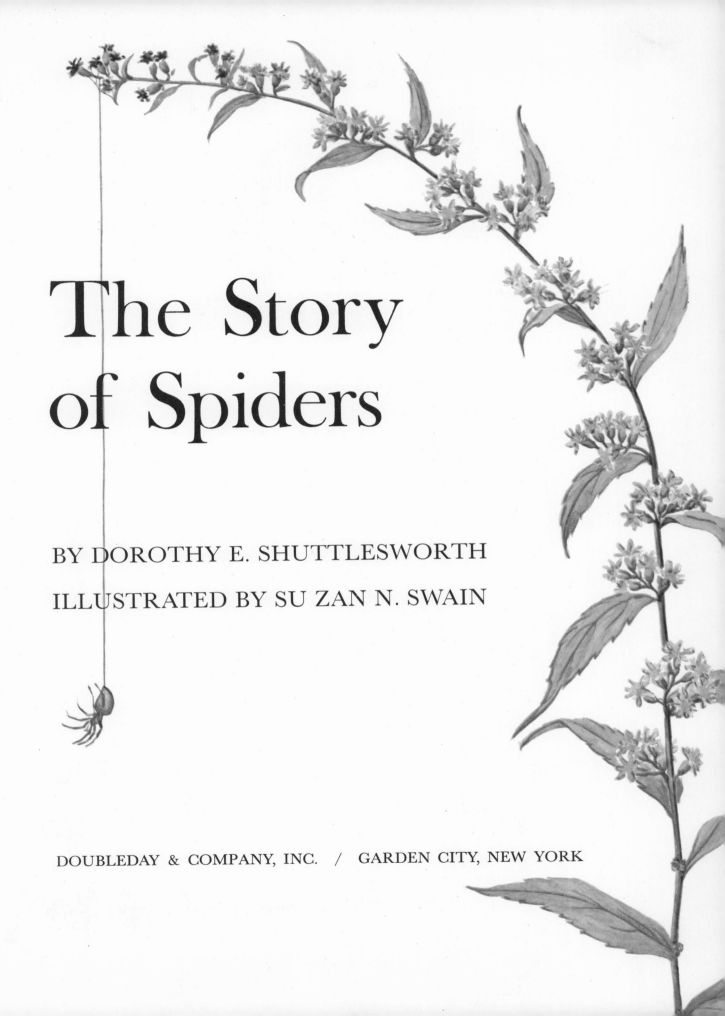

The Story of Spiders

BY DOROTHY E. SHUTTLESWORTH

ILLUSTRATED BY SU ZAN N. SWAIN

DOUBLEDAY & COMPANY, INC. / GARDEN CITY, NEW YORK

The warmest appreciation of artist and author goes to Dr. Willis J. Gertsch, Curator of Insects and Spiders, American Museum of Natural History, for reading the manuscript of this book and giving the benefit of his valued criticism, as well as aiding materially with specimens needed for illustrations. Gratefully acknowledged also is the kindness of Dr. Hugo G. Rodeck, Director of the Science Museum, University of Colorado at Boulder, Colorado, and his staff and Dr. Gordon Alexander and Dr. J. R. Hilliard of the Biology Department of the University, all of whom collected western specimens to be used as live models. A special salute is given Dr. C. M. Goethe of Sacramento, California, naturalist and conservationist, for his unceasing "propaganda" on behalf of spiders.

For my daughter Lee,
who loves all living things,
including spiders

Line sketch shows natural size of spider

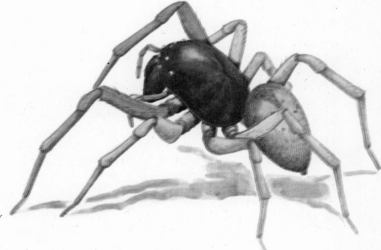

"RUNNING" SPIDER *Trachelas ruber*

Contents

CRAB SPIDER,
Misumenoides aleatorius,
feeding on moth

Mysterious and Misunderstood

Usually people know their friends from their enemies—but not always. And outstanding among our unrecognized friends are the spiders. By many they are considered nuisances or, still worse, horrifying creatures that should be exterminated whenever possible. How amazed these spider-haters would be if they studied the facts: Every year spiders do away with millions upon millions of insects such as locusts and grasshoppers that would destroy grain crops, and with such consumers of green leaves as beetles and caterpillars, as well as with troublesome mosquitoes and flies. One authority stated the case in these words: "If it were not for the number of spiders everywhere, all living creatures except defoliating (leaf-eating) caterpillars might face starvation."

It is generally understood that insects must be kept under control, and it is also well known that man-made insecticides present many problems because they poison animal life other than the intended victims. Therefore we should be deeply appreciative of our spider allies, which perform this service with no ill effects whatever to ourselves. If the wide extent of their insect control seems exaggerated, let us consider the

5

numbers in which they exist. A count made in one grassy acre in England turned up more than *two million* individual spiders. Though this is an exceptional abundance, any area of that size is likely to be inhabited by many thousands. Not only are spiders numerous, they are found almost anywhere. As everyone who has dusted away cobwebs knows, some types flourish indoors, others live outdoors but close to buildings. In fields they make their homes on tall plants and low shrubs, in forests they take refuge under dried leaves and fallen logs. Any piece of bark or stone may serve as a spider shelter. We may find them near water and even on it, in dry country, in underground caves, and on mountaintops.

Yet in spite of their abundance the true nature of spiders has remained little known to the average person, who believes they are sinister and aggressive and usually capable of a deadly bite. This ignorance has led to many misunderstandings about them —and the misunderstandings have woven about them an aura of mystery. Through the ages, in countless stories, spiders have been connected with sinister, unhealthy activities and places.

In truth a spider is a timid creature, most anxious to avoid contact with man. It bites only when hurt or frightened, and usually will walk over a person's skin without making any effort to bite. In fact the majority of spiders we might come across, being small, are not capable of breaking through the skin of a human; their biting apparatus is not strong enough. But the size of a spider is no clue to the serious nature of a bite it might inflict. Large wolf spiders will cause no greater pain nor in-

SPIDER PORTRAITS

"Variety" is the word for spiders. In appearance as well as in habits and abilities, various kinds show fascinating individuality. Here are pictured the faces of six different species, ranging from the shaggy tarantula to the sleek *Misumena*.

Lyssomanes viridis

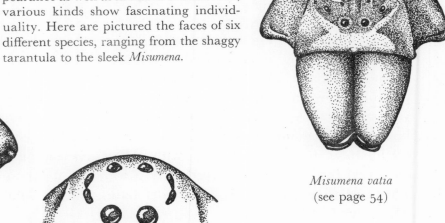

Misumena vatia
(see page 54)

(prepared after Kaston)

Tapinopa bilineata

6

convenience from poison than a wasp usually inflicts. On the other hand a black widow, the only spider native to the United States which can inflict poisoning of a truly serious nature upon a human, is small—no more than half an inch in length.

Because the unhappy result of the bite of a black widow is always given wide publicity, this little creature is known by name better than most spiders, and its habits have been frequently discussed. Yet even here guesswork has so often taken the place of research and knowledge that few facts are clearly understood. Black widow poisoning is often serious, but rarely is it fatal. Very young children and adults who are not in good physical condition suffer from it most acutely. If treated properly and promptly the ill effects usually lessen in a few hours and after a couple of days rest, the victim has completely recovered.

As to where black widows are found, every so often the news of one being found as far north as New York is treated as a startling discovery. Actually they have been found in every state in the Union as well as in parts of Canada. They are most common, however, in parts of the South and West of our country. Though much attention is given to any trouble a black widow may cause, little credit is awarded these remarkable creatures for the way they serve us. You will read about this in a later chapter.

Probably the most general misunderstanding of all about spiders is the idea that they are "queer insects." To understand why they should not be considered insects, nor even closely related to them, let us look at the position spiders occupy in the animal kingdom.

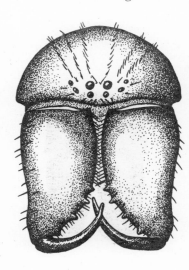

WATER SPIDER
Argyroneta aquatica
(after Crome)

A spider's "face" is the part of its head, which can be seen when observed from directly in front. It includes the eyes and the area between them as well as the space between the eyes and chelicerae—a pair of appendages with which the spider seizes and kills its prey. The spider's "head" consists of both face and chelicerae. Most frequently the eyes of a spider are near the front end of the head. The normal number is eight, but some species have only six, four, or two, and certain cave spiders are blind.

Tarantula

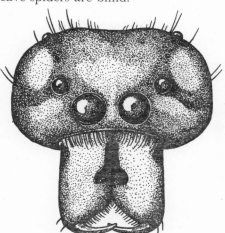

Metaphidippus exiguus
(after Kaston)

Spider Families and Their Relatives

The animal division large enough to include both spiders and insects is the group we know as "arthropods," and to this also belong such varieties as crustaceans (lobsters, crabs, shrimp, barnacles, and crayfish, for example), centipedes, and millipedes. In fact the variety of arthropods in this world is almost beyond belief, for estimates have been made revealing at least a million species. Though the classes of arthropods differ widely in size, shape, and habits there are some characteristics similar in all. Always the body (which lacks an internal skeleton) is encased in a hard outer coating; always it is divided into segments. Between the body segments and the legs the coating remains soft enough so that movement is easily possible. Growth is not restricted by the hard covering because at intervals the young growing arthropod sheds its outer skeleton and starts producing a new one.

Among the most famous of arthropods are the trilobites, which flourished when the world was young. Though they have been extinct for millions of years, countless fossils have been discovered which prove their abundance and importance in the prehistoric world. Centipedes, though not frequently seen, are considered intriguing because of their popular name: "hundred-legs." Do they or do they not have an even hundred? They may, but on the other hand they may have more than three hundred

A SPIDER'S ANATOMY

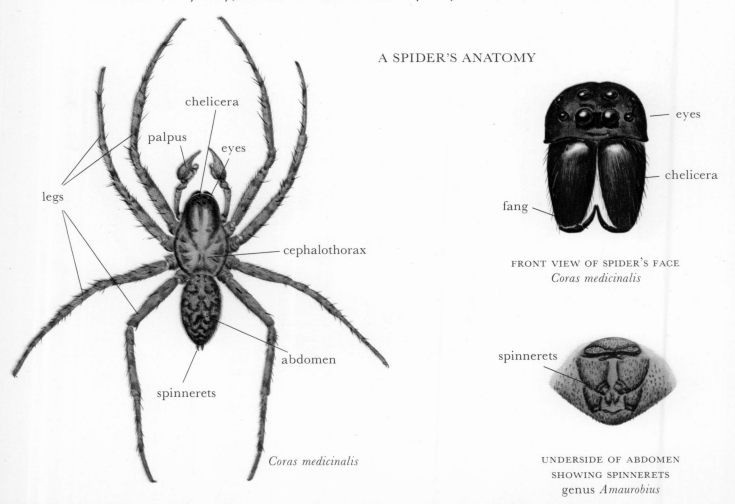

legs

palpus

chelicera

eyes

cephalothorax

abdomen

spinnerets

Coras medicinalis

eyes

chelicera

fang

FRONT VIEW OF SPIDER'S FACE
Coras medicinalis

spinnerets

UNDERSIDE OF ABDOMEN
SHOWING SPINNERETS
genus *Amaurobius*

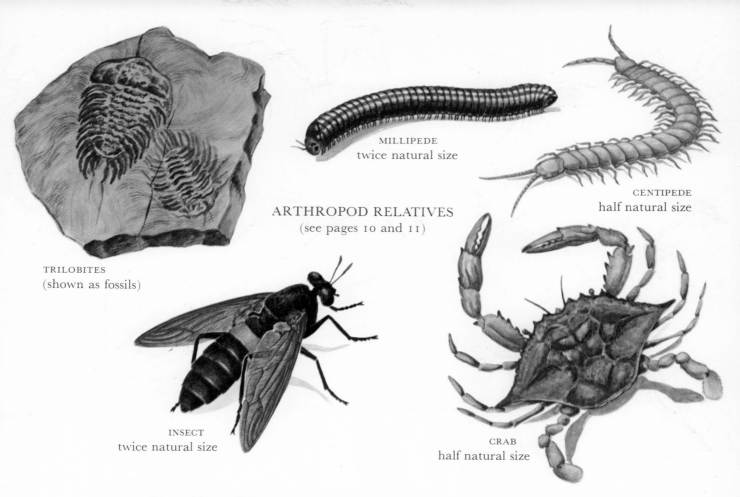

MILLIPEDE
twice natural size

CENTIPEDE
half natural size

ARTHROPOD RELATIVES
(see pages 10 and 11)

TRILOBITES
(shown as fossils)

INSECT
twice natural size

CRAB
half natural size

or a mere thirty. From thirty to seventy is most usual. The "thousand-leggers," as the millipedes are described, have numerous legs but fewer by far than the name suggests—fewer, in fact, than the centipedes.

Its number of legs is an important clue in knowing a spider from an insect. A fly, a bee, or any other insect has six; a spider has eight. Another difference to look for is the division of the bodies. The insect has three distinct parts: head, thorax, and abdomen. The head of a spider is fused with the thorax so that there are only two main divisions. Other differences are: Spiders are never equipped with wings, while insects usually are. Spiders do not have antennae, or feelers, whereas insects do. A spider usually has eight simple eyes, never compound eyes, as do the insects. Still another notable characteristic is the lack of true jaws. A spider does not chew and swallow its prey, but crushes it with a pair of nippers (known as the chelicerae), which are attached to the head. Then it gives out a liquid which digests the food so that it may be sucked into the stomach.

It is not so easy to compare the internal structure of spider and insect, but the differences are many. As we think of a spider's silk production we realize that apparatus to create this material must be present in the body. Few adult insects produce silk and in certain insect larvae, such as caterpillars, that do the production glands are located in the head and strands emerge from an opening on the lower lip. With spiders the glands are in the abdomen and the strands of silk come out of openings on spinning fingers at the hind end.

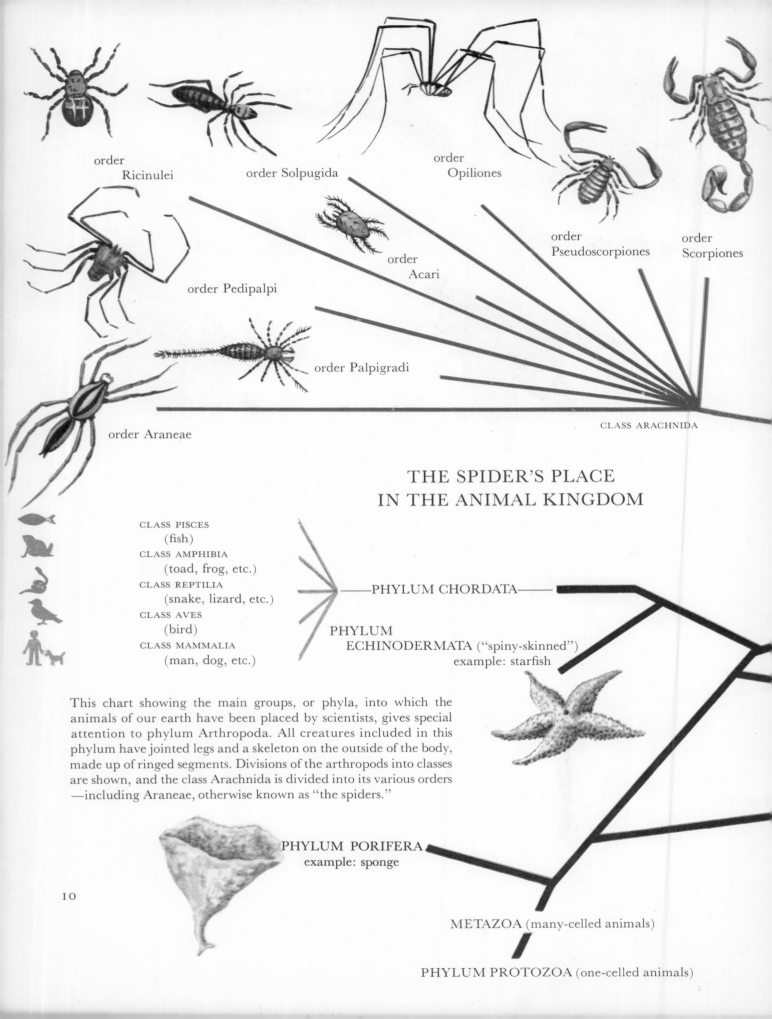

order
Ricinulei

order Solpugida

order
Opiliones

order
Pseudoscorpiones

order
Scorpiones

order Pedipalpi

order
Acari

order Palpigradi

order Araneae

CLASS ARACHNIDA

THE SPIDER'S PLACE
IN THE ANIMAL KINGDOM

CLASS PISCES
(fish)

CLASS AMPHIBIA
(toad, frog, etc.)

CLASS REPTILIA
(snake, lizard, etc.)

CLASS AVES
(bird)

CLASS MAMMALIA
(man, dog, etc.)

PHYLUM CHORDATA

PHYLUM
ECHINODERMATA ("spiny-skinned")
example: starfish

This chart showing the main groups, or phyla, into which the animals of our earth have been placed by scientists, gives special attention to phylum Arthropoda. All creatures included in this phylum have jointed legs and a skeleton on the outside of the body, made up of ringed segments. Divisions of the arthropods into classes are shown, and the class Arachnida is divided into its various orders —including Araneae, otherwise known as "the spiders."

PHYLUM PORIFERA
example: sponge

10

METAZOA (many-celled animals)

PHYLUM PROTOZOA (one-celled animals)

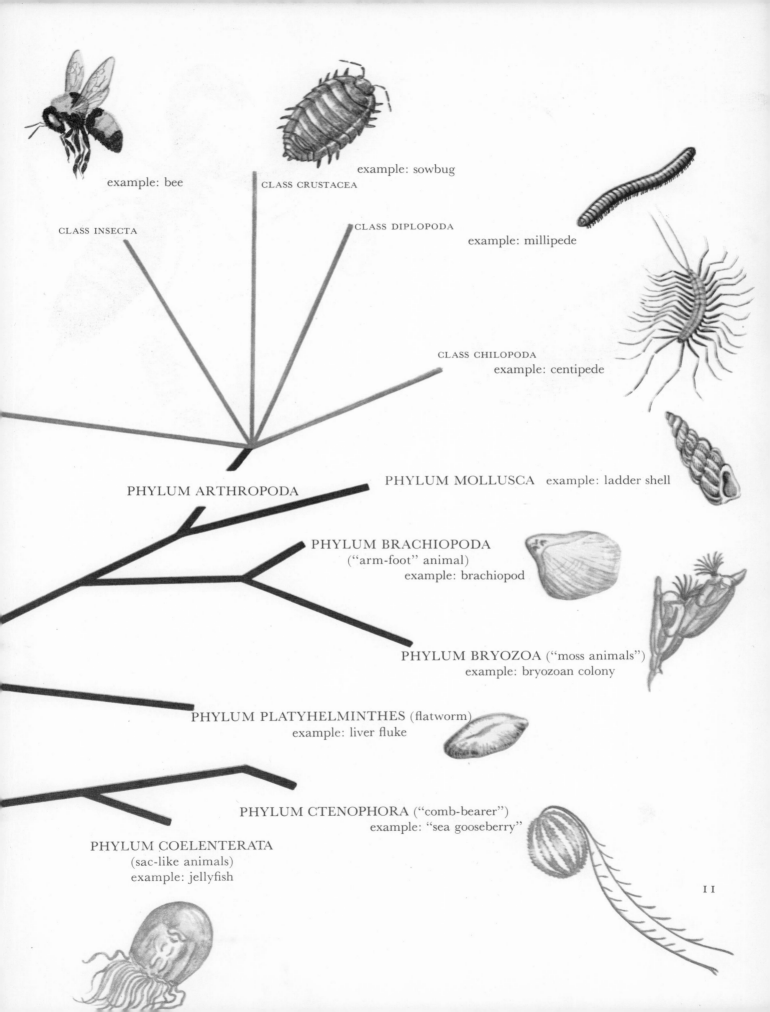

example: bee

CLASS INSECTA

CLASS CRUSTACEA

example: sowbug

CLASS DIPLOPODA

example: millipede

CLASS CHILOPODA
example: centipede

PHYLUM ARTHROPODA

PHYLUM MOLLUSCA   example: ladder shell

PHYLUM BRACHIOPODA
("arm-foot" animal)
example: brachiopod

PHYLUM BRYOZOA ("moss animals")
example: bryozoan colony

PHYLUM PLATYHELMINTHES (flatworm)
example: liver fluke

PHYLUM CTENOPHORA ("comb-bearer")
example: "sea gooseberry"

PHYLUM COELENTERATA
(sac-like animals)
example: jellyfish

11

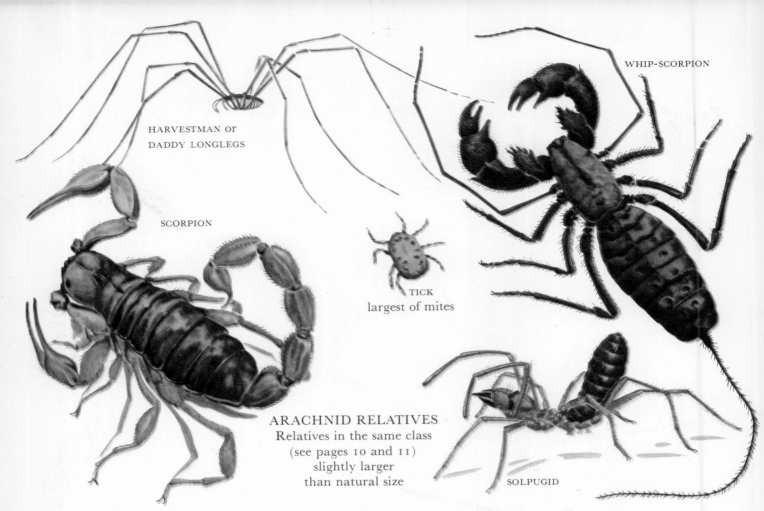

HARVESTMAN or
DADDY LONGLEGS

SCORPION

TICK
largest of mites

WHIP-SCORPION

ARACHNID RELATIVES
Relatives in the same class
(see pages 10 and 11)
slightly larger
than natural size

SOLPUGID

When we narrow the broad field of arthropods to a group that includes only spiders and several close relatives, we find they are named "arachnids"—a word taken from the Greek for spider. Among these relatives is the daddy longlegs, one of the most easily recognizable of small creatures because of its long, thin legs. Unlike the spiders, "daddy" does not spin silk, and its whole body structure consists of a single unit. Because it is seen in great numbers around harvest time it is often called by the name "harvestman." Harvestmen are entirely harmless; they are scavengers that feed largely on dead insects, although they may kill small ones and also suck juice from soft vegetables and other foods.

Another close relative is the scorpion—noted for its ability to "sting with its tail." The seriousness of such a sting varies with the species of scorpion. Two species out of nearly sixty in the United States whose poison really is a menace to humans are found in Arizona. There are also several scorpionlike creatures, such as the whip scorpions and sun scorpions.

Most numerous of the arachnids are the mites, many of which are real trouble-makers. The tiniest of them suck plant juices, causing blemishes to appear on leaves. A more serious problem to people are the harvest mites. In their larvae stage, when they are known as redbugs or chiggers, they attach themselves to the skin, causing violent irritation. Ticks, the largest of the mites, attack man as well as beast. Not only do some of these mites cause great discomfort but they may transmit disease.

While the term *Arachnida* is used for all these—the daddy longlegs, scorpions, and mites as well as spiders—the spiders alone belong to the order *Araneae*. This scientific name is more easily remembered when we connect it with Arachne, the heroine of a famous Greek legend. Arachne is said to have lived in Greece many centuries ago. So great was her skill in weaving, the legend relates, that people from far and near, and even woodland nymphs, came to see the products of her loom. Finally Arachne became tremendously enthused over her ability and challenged Athene, the goddess of weaving and handicrafts to compete with her. Athene accepted, producing a tapestry which showed the warfare of the gods. Arachne wove a gorgeous tapestry picturing the gods' love of adventure. It was done with such perfection that Athene was enraged, and destroyed it with a blow from her own spinning shuttle. The end of the story has been told from two different points of view. In one, the goddess turns Arachne into a spider and "condemns" her to perpetual spinning. In another version the goddess decrees death for Arachne but then repents and bestows upon her the favor of being a spider that may spin silk endlessly.

Our word "spider" does not come from a Grecian background; it had its origin in the German *spinner,* meaning "one who spins."

The order *Araneae,* though devoted solely to spiders, has tremendous variety. More than thirty thousand different species are known, and at least two thousand of these species live in our own country!

13

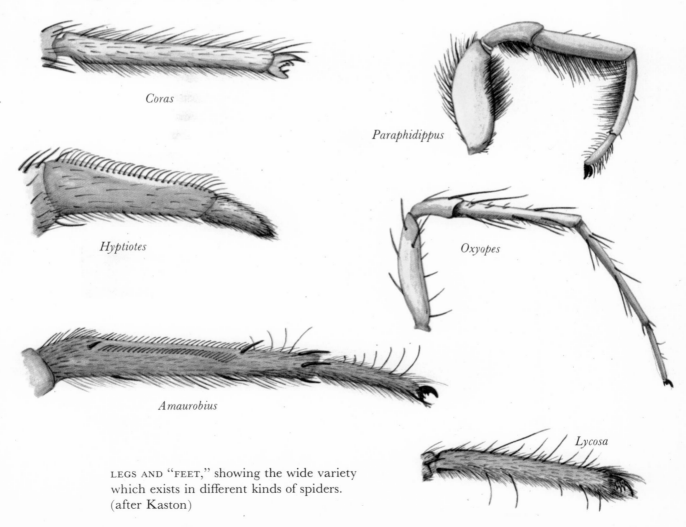

Coras

Paraphidippus

Hyptiotes

Oxyopes

Amaurobius

Lycosa

LEGS AND "FEET," showing the wide variety which exists in different kinds of spiders. (after Kaston)

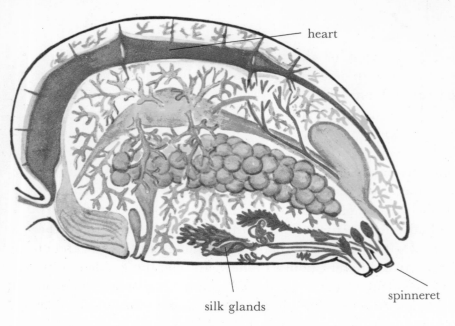

heart

silk glands

spinneret

CROSS SECTION OF SPIDER'S ABDOMEN

A single spinneret

Foot of garden spider showing toothed claws which manipulate silk threads

Living Silk Factories

The strength of spider silk, so delicate in appearance, is surprisingly great. A strand can be stretched as much as one half its normal length before breaking, and has a tensile strength surpassed only by fused quartz fibers. Some strands are stronger than others, the strength to some extent depending on the speed with which they are drawn out of the spider's body. The greater the speed, the greater the strength. There are other variations, too. Most of the silken threads are not single fibers but are made up of two or more strands. A fiber may be as fine as a millionth of an inch in thickness but more often it is ten or twenty times as thick, and the grouping of these fibers naturally produces threads of a variety of thicknesses. Also some fibers are sticky while others are not.

Although we are likely to think first of a web when we consider why a spider needs silk, this is only one of many uses to which their silk is put. Spiders use it for trap-lines, draglines, ballooning lines, for trap-door covers to underground retreats, for egg sacs and nursery webs, for chambers in which to hibernate or to mate, for the many types of webs in which food is ensnared, and for entangling and swathing their prey. Silk for all these purposes is not achieved with one type of gland; there are at least seven different types that equip the whole spider group. Some individual spiders have

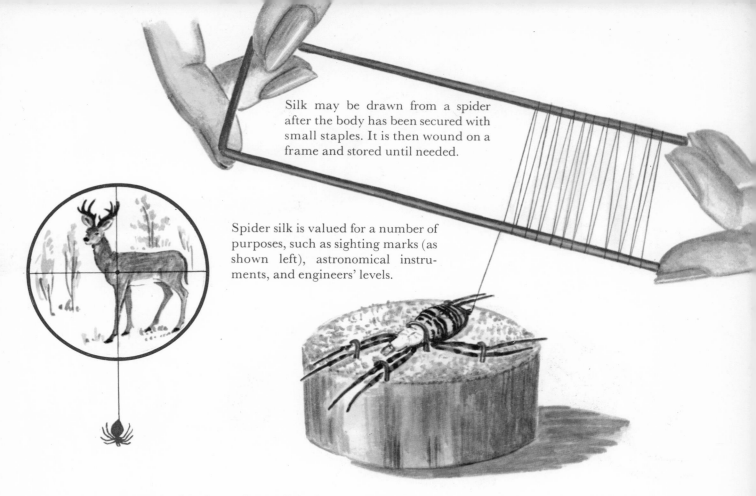

Silk may be drawn from a spider after the body has been secured with small staples. It is then wound on a frame and stored until needed.

Spider silk is valued for a number of purposes, such as sighting marks (as shown left), astronomical instruments, and engineers' levels.

as many as six kinds and possibly have more than six hundred separate glands; others have less than this.

The silk itself is a substance known as "scleroprotein." When produced in the glands it is a liquid; only when drawn outside the body does it harden into thread. Once it was thought that exposure to the air caused the hardening, but it now appears that the drawing-out process alone is responsible. To carry forward the work done by the glands, a spider is equipped with spinnerets, usually six in number. These are as flexible as fingers; they can be extended, compressed, and in general be used like human hands. In the "spinning field," where the spinnerets are grouped, single threads are combined into various thicknesses, and some of the dry strands may be coated with a sticky substance. Thus a finished strand may be thin or thick, dry or sticky. It may also have the form of a beaded necklace. For the latter type the spider spins rather slowly and, pulling out the sticky thread, lets it go with a jerk. The fluid thus is arranged in globules spaced along the finished line.

The thread known as the dragline may well be thought of as a spider's "life line" for it acts as a lifesaver under all sorts of conditions. No matter where or how far a spider travels, the dragline goes along, reeling out from spinnerets at the rear of the body. It forms part of the construction of webs, it holds its little manufacturer securely in difficult places, it aids in escaping from enemies. For a spider resting in a web the dragline makes possible a quick drop and hide-out in the vegetation. It enables active hunting spiders to leap from buildings, cliffs, or any high point in complete safety.   15

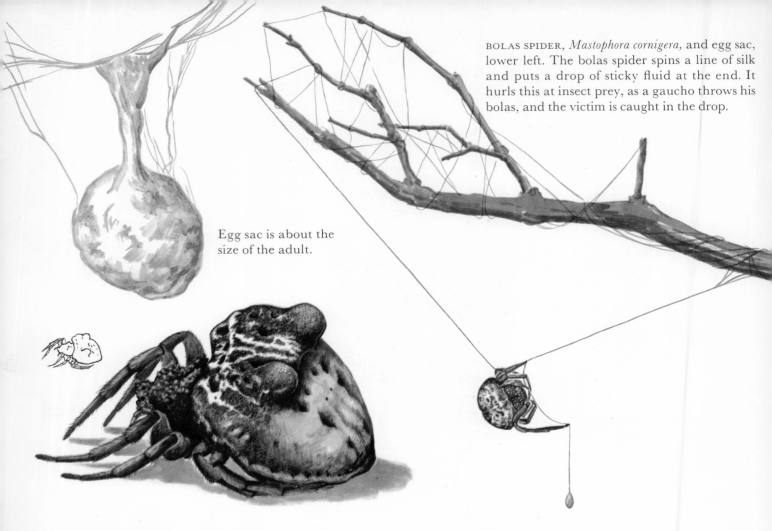

Egg sac is about the size of the adult.

Instead of falling, they float smoothly on the dragline. The dragline is never a single thread; the simplest type is made up of two rather large strands, but it may have four or even many threads stuck close together.

Observing the truly remarkable spinning ability of spiders we may wonder why their silk, rather than that of the silkworm, is not of great commercial importance. One reason lies in the varying thickness of spider thread. Also it is more difficult to work with, and, because it does not stand up well in the weaving process, it lacks the luster of insect silk. Besides all this the problems of housing and feeding large numbers of spiders are great compared with supporting silkworms. Nevertheless some remarkable studies have been made to explore the possibilities of having these little spinners work for man. In one, a hundred and fifty yards of silk thread were reeled from a spider in an hour and a quarter. This may seem a goodly production, yet at best more than four hundred spiders would be needed to create one square yard of commercial silk. Half that number of silkworms could accomplish the same production!

Primitive people have used spider silk in a number of ways. In New Guinea it is still valued for the making of fishing nets and lures and such articles as bags, head-dresses that will keep off the rain, and caps. These are not fashioned from single strands but from matted, twisted threads. The primitive natives of North Queensland, Australia, look to spiders for their fishing equipment. One way they use them is to entangle one end of a thin switch in a web, then, using a weaving motion, they twist the coarse silk lines into a single strand which may be more than a foot long. They use the spider itself as bait, crushing it over one end of the silken strand and tossing bits of the body into shallow water. The strand of silk is then trailed through the same area. As a fish rises to this bait its teeth become entangled in the invisible strands of silk and it is easily pulled out of the water. Most fish caught in this manner are no more than two inches long, but it is claimed that such silken fishing poles can hold more than half a pound in weight.

Besides being helpful to primitive people, spider silk has proved useful to the makers of such complicated instruments as astronomical telescopes, guns and engineers' levels. The fibers, being very fine yet strong and able to withstand extremes of weather, are excellent for sighting marks. During the Second World War there was considerable demand for spider fiber for surveying and laboratory instruments. The silk would be reeled from the spinnerets of living spiders, then stored on especially constructed frames until needed. Black widow spiders were used to a great extent for this silk production, although the common house orb weavers, the gardens orb weavers and others all help to provide the silk employed for specialized purposes.

There is one drawback to the use of spider silk in industry: It is likely to sag in a humid atmosphere. For this reason filaments of platinum or engraving on glass plates take its place in such instruments as periscopes and bomb sights.

Stick with a strand of twisted spider silk.

Unique fishing methods are made possible by spiders. In one, as described in "Two Years among New Guinea Cannibals" by E. A. Pratt, the natives set up a long bamboo pole, bent into a loop at one end.

A spider may spin its web over this convenient frame, thus forming a fisherman's net.

Steatoda borealis, a member of the family *Theridiidae* and its irregular mesh web.

The Web

Spiders are noted for web-building, yet many kinds never use their talents in this way. Instead of building silken traps they hunt their prey, stalking and leaping on their victims or hiding and pouncing on them. But before we meet those that do not make a web let us look at this marvel of the animal kingdom that is used as a symbol for the whole spider tribe.

Webs vary in style from the irregular cobweb that neat housewives constantly dust away, to the beautiful silken orbs that we so often find in a garden. There are four general types: besides the irregular mesh and the orb, we find funnel webs and sheet webs. Also, webs may be a combination of these separate types. Until they reach full growth male as well as female spiders spin silk and construct webs. However after their last molt the males no longer engage in spinning but often linger on or near the webs of their mates.

Messy as an irregular mesh web may appear, it is nevertheless built on a definite plan and is very efficient. The central maze is a widespread trap. Within this may be a densely woven sheet, combining such materials as leaves and grains of sand with the silk; it serves as a shelter for the little builder. Anchoring the maze firmly to supports are long guy lines which have small knobs of sticky silk near their base. When a small insect brushes against a sticky line it is snared, and as it struggles, the line breaks and tethers the victim. The common house spider and other members of the family *Theridiidae* prepare webs of this type.

18

The sheet web has been developed on a platformlike plan, with the webbing closely woven on a horizontal plane. A "platform" results and on this insects jump, fly, or drop, often being stopped in their flight by lines which the spider has crisscrossed above the platform. After building the platform, or sheet, the spider clings to its underside. Sometimes it constructs another sheet below so that it is sandwiched between two silken barriers. When victims land on the top sheet it pulls them through the silk. Sheet webs are built to last a long time. When they are damaged a few hours of work on the part of the spider usually puts them in working order again. Among the best known of the sheet-web weavers are those in the genus *Erigone,* about which you will read later.

Even more permanent than these sheet webs is the handiwork of the funnel-web spiders. Outside the retreat in which it lives, a member of this family starts to spin its webbing until a smooth runway is created. If this is on the ground, it suggests a sheet; if suspended from vegetation, a tiny hammock. In either case, it looks like a good landing field to insects. However, upon alighting they find themselves bogged down in a soft trap and they are quickly attacked by the spinner, which has been waiting at the mouth of its funnel retreat. As one of these spiders grows to adulthood, and as long as it remains active, it continues to add to its structure. Gradually a thin small mesh becomes a large thick blanket. In the autumn the webs are at their peak and, especially when covered with dew, may be seen spreading over acres of grasslands like dainty fairy-woven carpeting. The family *Agelenidae* represents the funnel-web weavers.

19

GRASS SPIDER, family *Agelenidae*
and its funnel-web.

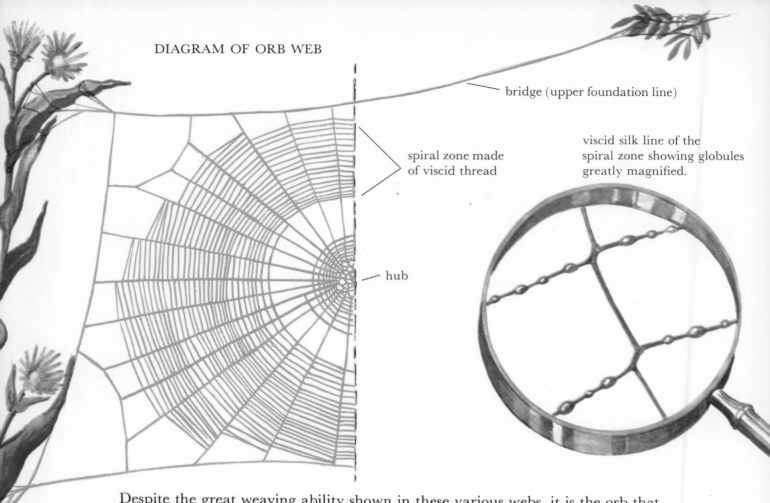

bridge (upper foundation line)

spiral zone made of viscid thread

viscid silk line of the spiral zone showing globules greatly magnified.

hub

Despite the great weaving ability shown in these various webs, it is the orb that is the real marvel of the spider world. Poets liken it to beautiful lace; engineers who understand construction problems look with wonder and respect at the complicated structures fashioned by these little creatures, which may be considered the original inventors of the suspension bridge.

Let us watch a garden spider, one of a number of the orb weavers, to see how this expert construction artist works. First she establishes her suspension bridge—one on which the whole web will hang. This is done in one of two ways: From an elevated perch she spins out a thread, letting it float through the air until it catches on some object, then she pulls it tight and fastens it with a disk of small threads. Or she may fasten the end of her silk to the elevated spot, carry the thread down one side of the area to be covered by the web, climb up again to a point suitable as the other end of the bridge, and here fasten the silk. With the bridge line established she strengthens it with additional thread, then drops to a lower point and fastens a silken line to an anchor such as grass or twig. To this she adds another line; then, holding her silk line free, she climbs again to the bridge, walks along it to a desirable position, attaches and tightens the third thread. Now three foundation lines form a triangle in which the round, or orb-shaped, trap can be placed. While the lines may form a triangle, they often are modified to rectangular or other forms.

The trap is begun by dropping a line across the framework, pulling it tight, then walking halfway across it. From this spot, which will be the center of the orb, she begins

20

to spin and to the frame attaches lines that resemble the spokes of a wheel. She also gives attention to strengthening the center area or hub. Next, working very fast, she runs spiral lines around and around over the spokes—lines that will hold the spokes in place while she does the finishing work on the web. Because they serve only as a construction aid, these are known as the "scaffolding spiral."

Up to this point only dry silk is produced. Now the spider begins to spin sticky or "viscid" threads. First she may fill in corners; then slowly and carefully she puts down the sticky line in spiral form, attaching it to the spokes, and working toward the hub. As she comes close to this center she bites out the dry lines of the scaffolding and either kicks them out of the way or eats them. The web is now in working order, but many of the various kinds of orb-web spiders have their own finishing touches to add. Some of them spin a white, flossy zigzag band across the web or below the hub.

The weaver makes use of its trap by hanging downward or away from the web, holding on to dry lines with its tiny claws, waiting for a tug on the silk to indicate that a victim has been caught in the web. An oil on its body prevents its being held down by its own sticky lines. The struggles of a victim often break a web seriously. The spider may tie broken lines together immediately or do so later. Some orb weavers spin a new web almost nightly, keeping only the foundation lines; others use a web far longer, making repairs when necessary. Though certain spiders spin their webs in the early morning, more often is this work done at twilight.

It might seem that a large web, with its complicated and lovely design, would require endless time to build, but as a rule an hour is more than enough for the project.

THE TRIANGLE SPIDER *Hyptiotes cavatus* and its web. This spider not only sits on the web's foundation line waiting for a victim but actually swings it back and forth, thus increasing the chance of snaring an insect.

Many orb-weavers fold a leaf and line it with silk to form a nest. Usually this is located near the web and a trap line extending from web to nest informs the spider when a victim is caught. Below is shown one such nest made by *Aranea thaddeus,* known as the "lattice" spider because of the nest's resemblance to a beautiful Oriental lattice.

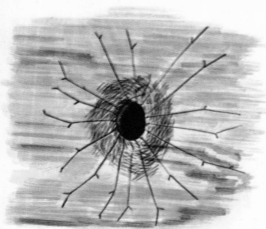

A nest by *Ariadna bicolor* in a hole caused by a nail being driven into wood. A slender tube extends downward suspended from a framework of threads at the entrance, as shown above.

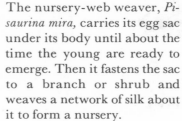

The nursery-web weaver, *Pisaurina mira,* carries its egg sac under its body until about the time the young are ready to emerge. Then it fastens the sac to a branch or shrub and weaves a network of silk about it to form a nursery.

Nests and Nurseries

Because we see webs often and in many places, we are apt to think of a web as the whole world of a spider—its trap, resting place, and retreat. However this is far from the case. Many kinds of spiders, including some which construct webs as well as those which do not, make snug nests for themselves. Actually there are more kinds of nests than there are webs.

One type of nest, made in the earth, is the work of certain wolf spiders. Their underground homes vary from a simple shaft with a silken lining to more complicated structures where an elevated lookout post may be built at the entrance. Even more remarkable are the hinged trap doors of the trap-door spiders and other burrowing tarantulas which are fashioned to close and conceal the underground burrow. Sometimes a second door is placed at a considerable distance from the main entrance.

A nest that is particularly strange is made by the purse-web spider. It is begun with a deep burrow in the earth at the foot of a tree. The spider lines this with silk and then continues the silk up the tree trunk, weaving it in the form of a tube and fastening it to the bark by threads. A tube may be as tall as ten inches and as wide as an inch, or much smaller. There is an opening at its top, although this is not easily seen because the silk is flattened and pressed together. The whole tube, in fact, is fairly well disguised by a covering of such materials as sand and moss which causes it to blend with the tree trunk.

Spiders from many different families meet their desire for a nest simply by rolling or folding a leaf and lining with silk the area that is enclosed.

22

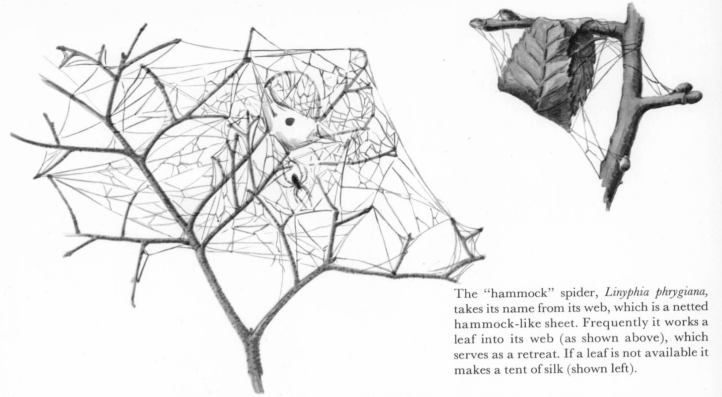

The "hammock" spider, *Linyphia phrygiana,* takes its name from its web, which is a netted hammock-like sheet. Frequently it works a leaf into its web (as shown above), which serves as a retreat. If a leaf is not available it makes a tent of silk (shown left).

Among the web-building spiders there are some that do live on the web and merely run away from it when they are disturbed. Others, however, build a nest near the web, in which they spend much of their time waiting for victims. Orb weavers are very likely to use the rolled-leaf type of nest, which they often build above or to one side of the web, with a trapline leading from it to the center of the orb.

Only a few spiders have social habits. One is a tiny spider, just one sixth of an inch long, which enjoys a community home rather than living by itself. It is known as the *mosquero* in the regions of Mexico where it is found. *Mosqueros,* working together, cover each branch of an entire tree with an inner layer of dry silken threads and from this hang an outer envelope of sticky silk. Often such a nest is more than six feet square. After a season of egg laying the adults look for new territory. The people of certain Mexican villages put these nests to good use as fly traps. They remove a branch of webbing from the tree and hang it from the ceiling of their home. The immense swarms of flies that appear during the rainy season are cut down to a great extent as they light upon the sticky silk threads of the nest and are quickly pulled within by the hungry spiders.

Such community life is unusual with spiders; however it is their custom to lay eggs in masses—never singly—and to enclose the egg mass in a sac. It seems that far back in time, when the spider tribe was just becoming established on earth, the idea was tried of using a silken covering for eggs. Through the ages that followed, many spiders developed this protective idea to an amazing degree, and today most kinds of spiders have a set of glands especially used for the production of egg sacs. Various species use their own special design, sometimes decorating with wood, leaves, and stones so that a sac is less easily seen, or plastering it with mud. The silk used for sac making is less elastic and not so strong as dragline silk.

23

It is not surprising to find that certain of the web-spinning spiders construct the most handsome and efficient egg sacs. One of these is the orange *Argiope*. The female begins her project by fastening yellowish silk threads to a structure so that a simple roof is formed. To this she adds a thick mass of fluffy yellowish silk, then a layer of dark brown silk. Working in an upside-down position, she lays her eggs against this brownish sheet. Then, as the mass of eggs hangs as a yellow ball, she spins a thin but strong covering over them, joining it to the brown disk. Next she spins a brownish or yellowish-brown silk and, using her hind legs as a comb, pulls it into loose loops and pats it into a soft blanket around the egg mass. Still the structure is not complete; she now works on a covering of white or yellow silk, which is very closely spun and smooth. Soon this hardens and looks much like parchment. The eggs at last are covered to her satisfaction, and mother *Argiope* can rest—after several hours of steady work.

While many spiders produce all their eggs at one laying and thus only need construct one egg sac, there are others that lay eggs over a period of time and make a series of egg sacs. With many species the mother dies soon after her egg-sac work is completed; when the babies hatch they are "on their own" from the beginning. However there are interesting exceptions to this rule. In some species the egg sac is made within the web and when the young emerge they live there for some time, enjoying their mother's protection and the food caught in her web.

Another variation is the kind of spider that carries the egg sac with her. A wolf spider does this, dragging the sac wherever she goes until the spiderlings emerge. The babies immediately crawl on the mother's back and are carried about until ready for an independent life. There is another spider, known as the nursery-web weaver or fisher spider, which like the wolf spider carries the egg sac but which also provides a nursery. When it is almost time for the young to hatch, the mother fastens the sac to the top of a plant and spins a web about the leaves that surround it. She then stands guard close by, ready to protect her brood against all enemies.

24

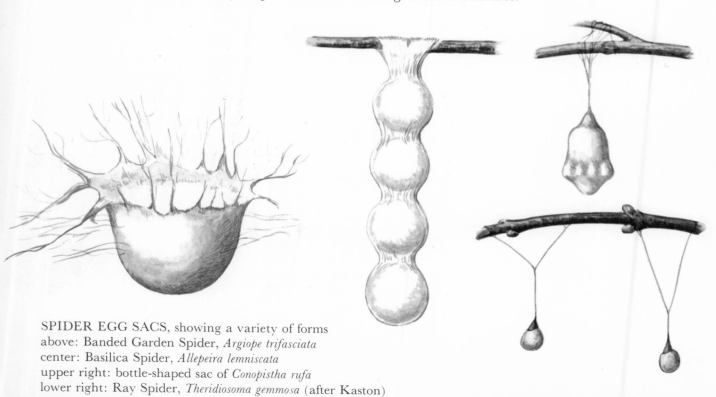

SPIDER EGG SACS, showing a variety of forms
above: Banded Garden Spider, *Argiope trifasciata*
center: Basilica Spider, *Allepeira lemniscata*
upper right: bottle-shaped sac of *Conopistha rufa*
lower right: Ray Spider, *Theridiosoma gemmosa* (after Kaston)

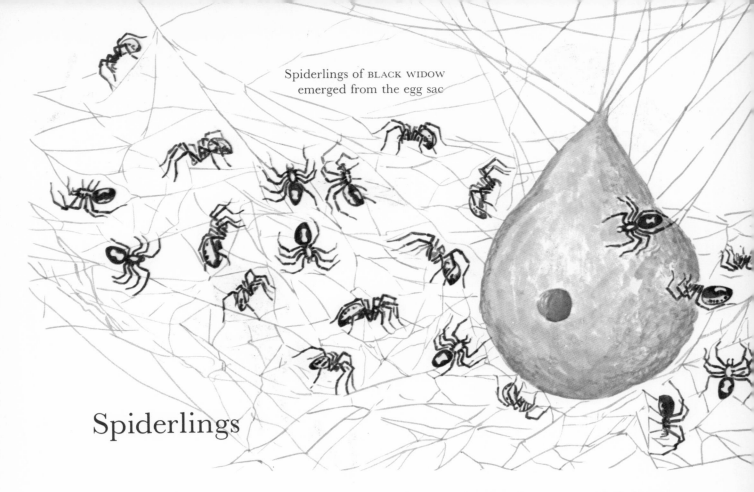

Spiderlings of BLACK WIDOW
emerged from the egg sac

Spiderlings

To a baby hatching in a spider egg sac, the world must seem a very crowded place. Hundreds of brothers and sisters develop at about the same time and are closely packed together. Nevertheless they do not leave the sac immediately. First they undergo a molt, and as they shed their first skin they emerge with a true spider form. The legs become longer and more slender, and tiny claws appear. The youngsters now have the ability to spin silk but have little use for it.

The weather plays a large part in deciding how long spiderlings stay in the sac. In northern areas when eggs are laid late in the fall, it is usual for them to remain there throughout the winter. However the young of many species leave soon after hatching. It was once thought that many baby spiders which hatched within a sac never lived to see the outside world but were devoured by brother and sister spiderlings. However there is no real evidence that such cannibalism takes place, and the theory is no longer credited. However there is no doubt but that cannibalism often exists among adult spiders. Some make a habit of preying on other spiders as a source of food, and many females destroy their own mates. But spider couples do not always part in this unhappy fashion!

When a family of young spiders is ready for the great wide world outside the cradle that has enclosed them they force a tear in its side. If the wall is very tough, a group of them usually cuts a round hole. Then one by one the spiderlings parade out into the open. Their problem now is to scatter in many directions so that a large number will not be trying to make a living in one small area. Usually they do this by "ballooning."

25

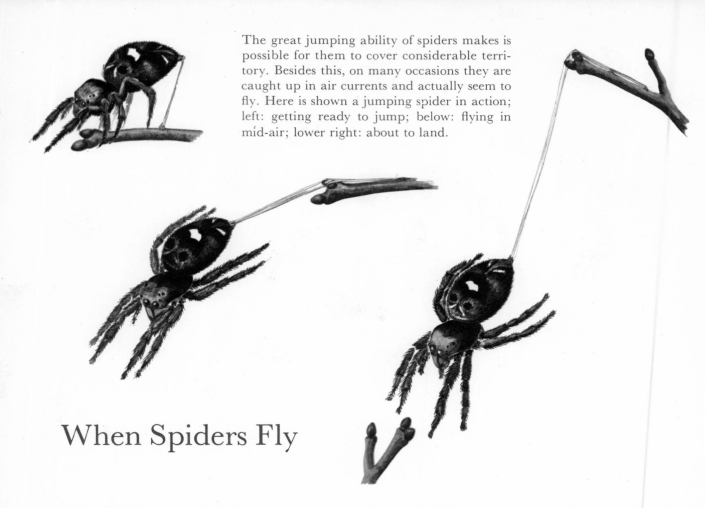

The great jumping ability of spiders makes is possible for them to cover considerable territory. Besides this, on many occasions they are caught up in air currents and actually seem to fly. Here is shown a jumping spider in action; left: getting ready to jump; below: flying in mid-air; lower right: about to land.

When Spiders Fly

Ballooning is a strange and wonderful example of animal instinct. Let us picture a group of spiderlings just freed from their egg sac. It would seem a real problem for them to explore the territory about them, for each to find a suitable home; but they find a way to disperse so that they are not overcrowded. Quietly, each makes its way to a high point on a weed or fence; there it faces the direction from which a breeze is blowing, stretches out its legs to the fullest extent, and tilts its abdomen upward. At once silk threads are drawn from the spinnerets by air currents, and they continue to stream out until the pull on the thread is strong enough to support the spider. Now the little creature loosens its hold on its perch and is pulled up into space to be air-borne toward some new area.

While ballooning is carried out during much of the year, it is largely an occurrence of the spring and fall when great numbers of spiderlings are coming out of their egg sacs. Because of their light weight, little spiders sometimes find themselves ballooning when they have no reason to do so; even some larger spiders may find themselves at the mercy of the breezes as the silk threads with which they are working carry them aloft. Occasionally, on days when the air is completely still, we may see spiderlings sail upward. This apparently is caused by a steady upward current of air from the warmed earth—a current strong enough to give altitude to a length of silk attached to an almost weightless bit of animal life. Small adult spiders also make a practice of

ballooning.

Air currents may take young spiders to great heights, but from the ballooning that has been observed, it seems the usual traveling altitude is about two hundred feet. The distance they go from their place of birth varies greatly. It might be only a few yards; on the other hand "flying" spiders have alighted on ships more than two hundred miles from any land. Small wonder that spiders are found in almost every land area of the world! Islands, mountaintops, and valleys all can be reached by balloon travel. Some kinds of spiders actually exercise a degree of control over their "space ship" by climbing on their threads and pulling in and winding up or letting out more silken filaments.

Not always are flights successful, however. A bump against some obstacle in its path may bring a spider down in an unsuitable place; and many would-be flyers become detached from their silk threads. Such a happening is the cause of "gossamer" —the large but dainty sheets of silk so often mentioned in poetry. Discarded threads, put out for flight but not used, are left hanging on a group of plants and become matted. One day a wind picks up the mass of threads and carries it away, and soon some distant spot is covered with a gossamer sheet. Sometimes a large field will be blanketed in this way but so delicate is the fabric that it is only seen when the sunlight hits it at a certain angle.

Almost, but not all, true spiders make use of ballooning when they are newly hatched. Tarantulas are among those which do not, apparently because of the large size of the young.

Somewhat of a mystery is the fact that although spiderlings of many sorts are tossed to the winds for distribution, when studies are made of spider populations they do not prove to be haphazard. To a great extent certain species are found only in certain areas and in certain kinds of situation. For example one species will be found only in bushes in the open while another is attached to houses. Since spiders use just about anything for food, and can weave their webs almost anywhere, we must wonder what causes them to show such decided preferences in their living quarters.

A courtship dance is carried out by many male spiders to attract a mate. Here are shown poses of two different jumping spiders as they perform their rituals. (adapted after Peckham)

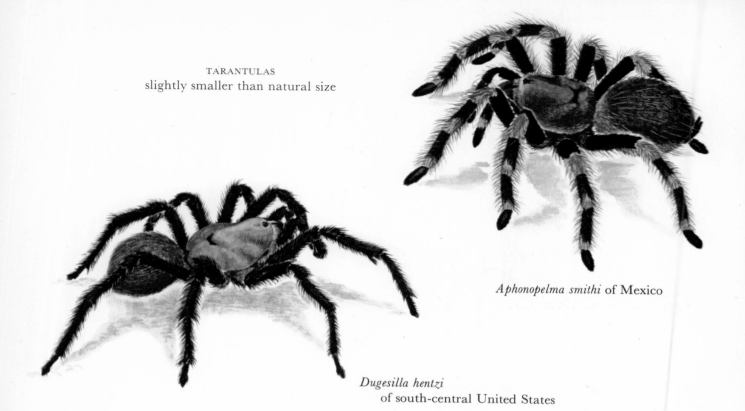

TARANTULAS
slightly smaller than natural size

Aphonopelma smithi of Mexico

Dugesilla hentzi
of south-central United States

Tarantula, the Giant

If a vote were taken to decide the spiders with the most fearsome appearance, the "honor" probably would go to the large, hairy spiders Americans call tarantulas but which Europeans call bird spiders. Not only are they thought of as being the largest, but they sometimes are covered with velvety wool and long silken hairs. Furthermore a general belief credits them with deadly poisoning powers.

Several of these ideas may be said to be untrue as well as being true, because there are tarantulas *and* tarantulas. The origin of the name is an outstanding example of how confusing superstitions and lack of knowledge can be: During medieval times, near the city of Taranto, Italy, a certain type of spider was quite common. Also common was the habit of wild dancing among the people; but eventually such dancing was forbidden by government authorities. Apparently in an effort to be able to continue their frenzied dances, some natives claimed they had been bitten by this kind of spider and the only cure was a style of music to which they could dance in an uncontrolled fever of excitement. The music became known as a "tarantella" and the spider was christened with the name tarantula. Actually it was a large wolf spider, belonging to the genus *Lycosa*. In recent years tests have been made as to the results of its bite, and no ill effects worthy of notice developed.

The genus *Lycosa* is a large one, and many species belonging to it are found in the Americas. Certain of them, native to South America and especially southern

28

Brazil, really are a menace to humans. They are quite likely to wander into a house during the night and find a resting place amid clothing. When someone puts on the clothes the spider is trapped and may bite in self-defense. Such a wound, depending on its location, may be very serious; fortunately a serum has been developed that treats the poisoning successfully.

We will look at some of the *Lycosa* found in the United States in our next chapter, but now will turn to what might be called the American tarantulas, which have little in common with the European wolf spider. To the American tarantula group belong some of the largest of all spiders. *Lasiodora* is one, with a body length of about three inches and a leg span (when legs are extended) of nearly ten inches. Its native home is Brazil. Of the thirty-some species of tarantula that live in the United States —mostly in the Southwest—many are dwarfs when compared to this imposing creature. For our native tarantulas in their natural surroundings, we must look carefully along an open area on a hillside, in mixed desert growth or along the fringes of cultivated land. Here we may discover one of their burrows. If a loose webbing covers the entrance it indicates the spider is at home, having spun the silken curtain after a night of hunting.

The burrow of a tarantula has need to be spacious, for in it the mother spins out a large sheet on which to deposit her eggs, which are both large and numerous. She covers these with a second sheet and binds the two edges together. Then for six or

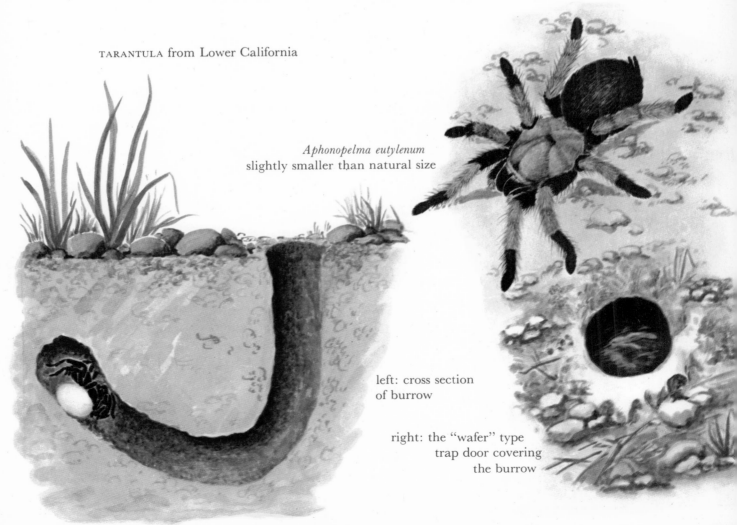

TARANTULA from Lower California

Aphonopelma eutylenum
slightly smaller than natural size

left: cross section
of burrow

right: the "wafer" type
trap door covering
the burrow

left: a "cork" type trap door, twice natural size, of *Bothriocyrtum californicum*, shown open. The trap-door spider can hold its door closed against the determined pull of many an enemy—successfully resisting a force one hundred forty times its own weight.

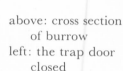

above: cross section
of burrow
left: the trap door
closed

seven weeks she keeps watch over the baglike egg sac, once in a while dragging it to the burrow's entrance so that the direct sunlight reaches it. When the spiderlings emerge they are in no great hurry to leave the burrow but finally they do, and look for protective covers such as stones and chips under which to hide. Soon they dig their own burrows. As has been mentioned, they are too large to use the ballooning method for reaching new homes.

The growing period for tarantulas is long; something like ten years is needed for them to become fully adult. During this time the male and female look almost exactly alike and each lives alone in matching burrows; but upon reaching full growth, and molting for the last time, the males become much darker than the females—and they develop a spirit of adventure. During late summer and fall they leave their long-occupied burrows and wander far and wide in search of a mate. With the end of the mating period, a male's life is usually completed. Even if he does not die a natural death, his mate is likely to kill him. The female, on the other hand, lives on and may survive as long as twenty-five or more years.

There is one type of tarantula which is known by another name because of its very special ability in building. This is the trap-door spider, found in our southern and western states. It is true that spiders of many other families dig burrows and may make covers for them, but these of the tarantula group are masters at tunneling. Also they are the real inventors of that bit of equipment so valuable to all builders—the hinge. As digging tools they use rows of large spines which grow along their jaws.

This rakelike formation makes it possible for them to cut and scrape away small bits of earth, which the spider rolls into balls and carries outside the burrow. The little builder then coats its walls with saliva and earth, making them smooth, firm, and waterproof. Only then does it create a silken lining. Usually the burrow is large enough at some point for the spider to reverse its position, turning around without venturing into the open. The entrance to the burrow is usually covered by a lid or door.

The door's inner surface has the same appearance as the lining of the burrow, being made of a firm layer of silk. And by continuing the silk from the lining into the silk that forms the foundation of the door, the spider makes a firm hinge! The door's outer surface is treated in a variety of ways, with the idea of disguising it. For example when a burrow is dug in moss-covered soil, the spider often plants moss on the lid. Or leaves and sticks may be used as camouflage. One kind of door, composed only of silk, is known as the "wafer" type; a second kind, in which soil is included with the silk, is the "cork" type. By grasping the inner surface the spider can hold the door closed against enemies with surprising strength. When ready to hunt, it pushes the door open and sits quietly until it can grasp a grasshopper, beetle, or other prey. Few trap-door spiders move very far away from their burrows.

Related to these tarantulas are several groups known as the "atypical" tarantulas. For the most part they live much farther north in the United States than do their

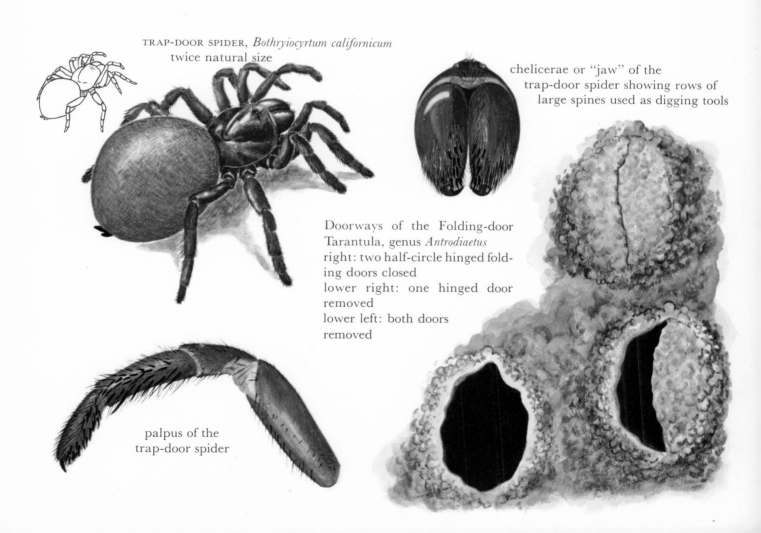

TRAP-DOOR SPIDER, *Bothryiocyrtum californicum*
twice natural size

chelicerae or "jaw" of the
trap-door spider showing rows of
large spines used as digging tools

Doorways of the Folding-door
Tarantula, genus *Antrodiaetus*
right: two half-circle hinged folding doors closed
lower right: one hinged door
removed
lower left: both doors
removed

palpus of the
trap-door spider

entrance to a turret-spider's burrow
Lycosa carolinensis twice natural size
(see page 34)

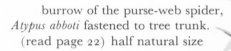

burrow of the purse-web spider,
Atypus abboti fastened to tree trunk.
(read page 22) half natural size

"typical" cousins. Another difference is that they are of more moderate size; most of them are a mere inch in length, or even smaller. They also are efficient burrowers, but only a few types have coarse spines on the jaws with which to rake.

One of the atypical group is the folding-door tarantula, found in various parts of the United States but chiefly in the Southeast. The name is based on this spider's plan for closing a burrow. Two hinged flaps of silk are made, one on each side, and these are drawn together to cover the opening. The spider opens them in the evening and is ready for its nightly hunting; in the morning it pulls them together. They meet in a straight line at the middle of the hole.

California is the home of another member of this group, the turret spider. It, like its relatives, makes a burrow, but instead of construction stopping at the ground's surface, it continues on upward. Sometimes a short tube of silk is formed, sometimes a long one, which may be worked right through moss or thick grass. At its end it is expanded into a wide lip. The spider sits in the entrance of this turret, in an excellent position to snatch at the hapless insects which come within its reach.

Purse-web spiders, numerous in Georgia and Florida and found also in woodlands from Florida to Texas and north to Massachusetts, have somewhat the same idea of building—that is, they continue the silken lining of a burrow up from the ground, fastening the tube that is formed to a tree trunk.

32

The "Wolves"

Anyone who thinks of spiders as sneaky characters because they make traps and lie in wait for their prey should lose no time making the acquaintance of the hunting spiders. Many are keen-eyed, bold, and swift-moving, although there are some hunters that venture from their retreats only after dark and their prey consists of small creatures they stumble on by chance.

Outstanding among the bold hunters are wolf spiders. They have been given the scientific name *Lycosa,* from the Greek word for wolf. The family is widespread indeed. You will remember that one of its members is the tarantula of Italy, which was falsely accused of causing a dancing sickness. In our own country *Lycosas* are found in nearly every region and in all kinds of surroundings—damp pasture lands, in fields, at the edges of woods, in grazing areas along roadsides, on dry hillsides and on prairies. In spite of their wandering ways, most *Lycosas* make some sort of retreat for themselves. It may be a simple excavation under log or stone, lined with silk and surrounded by a small wall of earth, sticks, or stones, or it may be a tubelike burrow in the earth, a foot or more deep.

33

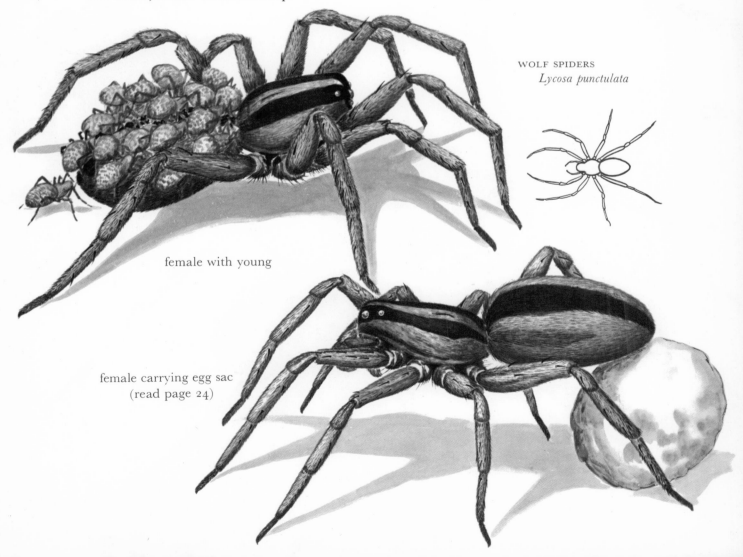

WOLF SPIDERS
Lycosa punctulata

female with young

female carrying egg sac
(read page 24)

A female *Lycosa* is among those spider mothers that carry their spiderlings pick-aback-fashion for some days after they emerge from the egg sac. Actually the little ones swarm over her body so that all but her head is covered. Nevertheless she carries on hunting activities as usual, and they must hang on to the best of their ability as she dashes after insects or flees from an enemy. The large *Lycosas* live for two or more years. During the winter the entrance to a burrow is securely closed with bits of leaves, sticks, and other scraps, fastened together with silk.

Lycosas wear a thick velvety coat of hair. It varies in color from black to gray or brown, and pale markings in stripes, patches, or spots form a variety of patterns. The upper part of the body is more softly colored and thus is apt to blend with the surroundings; the underside is often marked boldly with black stripes and patches.

Largest of our native wolf spiders, and one that may be found over the greater part of the United States, is *Lycosa carolinensis*. In northern areas this *Lycosa* grows to about an inch in length; in the south and southwest it is much larger. Another *Lycosa* of note is *Lycosa aspersa,* the "tiger wolf." It is a common burrowing type found from New England to the Gulf of Mexico and westward to Kansas. Distinguished by pale yellowish stripes on rich dark brown hair, it may be found in many open woodlands. Its burrow is a fine example of camouflage. At the entrance the spider builds a high para-

34

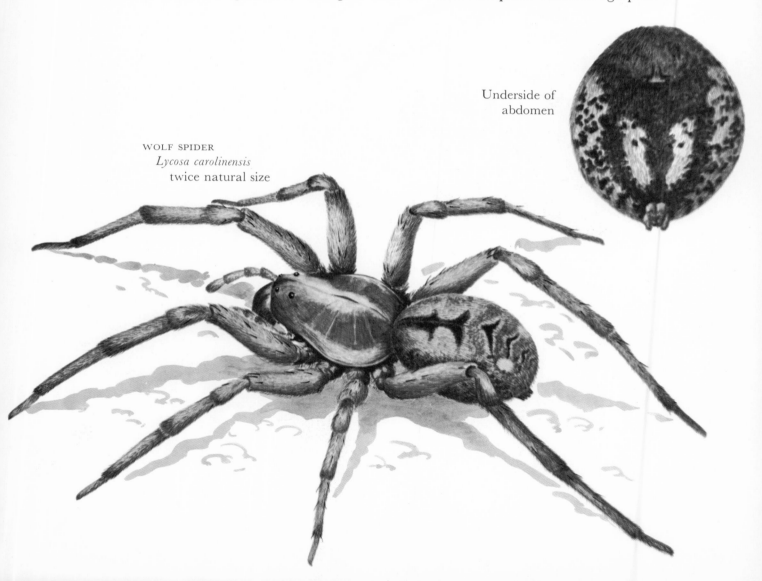

Underside of
abdomen

WOLF SPIDER
Lycosa carolinensis
twice natural size

Lycosa punctulata, very common from New England
to Florida, west to the Rockies
all twice natural size

TIGER WOLF SPIDER
Lycosa aspersa

left: female

above: male

pet of moss and debris, then over its top spins a canopy with a small opening at one side. As a finishing touch, bits of moss, soil, and leaves are strewn over the canopy—and the whole structure becomes quite unnoticeable in its woodland site. Another camouflage artist is *Lycosa lenta,* one of a number of "sand wolves." Though this lycosid may abound in sandy areas where you are spider hunting, you may look all day and not find one. Its pale grayish hair blends perfectly with the sand, and if one is discovered and disturbed it does a magical disappearing act. A quick somersault—a plunge into the sand—and it has gone without leaving a trace! Its secret is a flimsy hidden burrow covered with a trap door which is concealed with a coating of sand. The agile little creature dives into the burrow head first and closes the door with its legs. After dark, sand wolves may be found easily with the aid of a flashlight, which causes their eyes to gleam like tiny jewels.

One of the interesting wolf spiders that does not belong to this *Lycosa* group is the thin-legged *Pardosa.* Many species of *Pardosa* live in the United States, under a great variety of conditions. They do not use any retreat for long, but wander far and wide and often may be seen climbing over plants, like skilled acrobats. Many of them also have the ability to run easily over the water's surface; but for a still more aquatic type let us look at the fisher spiders—members of the *Dolomedes* group.

35

Fisher Spiders

Because the *Dolomedes* spiders make a habit of living near streams and ponds, we might expect them to be named "water spiders." As a matter of fact, they are often referred to in this way; however there is a European spider which is more completely devoted to an aquatic life, and the term water spider is best reserved for this particular kind. "Fisher" rightly suggests that the *Dolomedes* spiders like to live near water, and that they not only prey on aquatic insects but occasionally catch small fishes as well. *Dolomedes* does not actually swim, but can walk on the water with ease and remains beneath its surface for long periods of time.

A typical fisher is a large spider, gray or brown in color, but the most striking in appearance, and also the most truly aquatic, is *Dolomedes sexpunctatus*. This is a dark greenish-gray creature with a white band extending down each side of its body. Two rows of white spots decorate the abdomen and six dark dots are located at the front of the body. You may catch sight of *Dolomedes sexpunctatus*, legs outstretched, resting on the surface of stream or swamp in many parts of our country. It has a close relative in England known as the "raft spider" because of its habit of constructing a tiny raft out of silk and a few dead leaves. Although it can run over the water's surface, it often waits for its prey comfortably perched on this silken floating platform.

The European water spider, which belongs to a different genus than *Dolomedes*, builds even more amazingly to suit its particular habits. It constructs an underwater home—or, rather, homes. One is made to serve during summer months while another is provided for the winter. The little builder, *Argyroneta* by name, is most ordinary in appearance—plain brown in color and a mere half inch in length. Like other spiders, it has eight legs—none extra that might explain its swimming technique or its ability to work underwater. It is the only spider that can truly swim and move about in the water without being in contact with some submerged object.

FISHER SPIDER, *Dolomedes sexpunctatus,* slightly larger than natural size

36

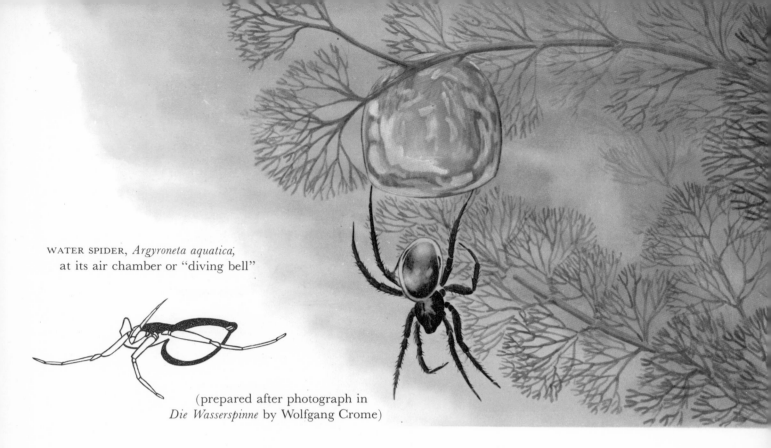

WATER SPIDER, *Argyroneta aquatica*,
at its air chamber or "diving bell"

(prepared after photograph in
Die Wasserspinne by Wolfgang Crome)

Argyroneta solves the problem of an oxygen supply by going up to the water's surface, raising her abdomen, and capturing an air bubble under it. She then dives below the surface, and if she remains quietly in one place one air bubble may last for several hours. It is more likely, however, that she will swim energetically, and this results in using up the oxygen supply more quickly.

The warm-weather home, built in the spring, begins as a small, closely woven platform of silk, suspended from nearby plants. The weaving finished, *Argyroneta* goes to the water's surface and traps a large air bubble under her abdomen. Brushes of long, curved hairs on her hind legs help to hold together her precious burden as she paddles downward until she reaches a spot just under the silken sheet. Here she releases the air which rises and pushes against the silk, causing it to puff out. More trips to collect air follow until finally the silk has taken on the form of a tiny diving bell, open at the bottom. *Argyroneta* then strengthens it with more weaving and by constructing additional supports.

The male *Argyroneta* may spin a smaller "diving bell" nearby that of his mate and join the two with a tunnel of silk, or he may share the chamber the female has made. When eggs are produced they are cradled in a sac and, thus protected, they hang in the upper part of the bell for about three weeks, when they hatch.

As winter approaches, *Argyroneta* selects a new building spot deeper in her pond or stream, often seeking a protective shelter such as an empty snail shell. Here she weaves a solidly constructed closed sac, and this is her home until spring returns. Because she is completely inactive the air supply she stores away is sufficient to last throughout the winter.

37

GREEN LYNX SPIDER
Peucetia viridans
with egg sac

The Lynx

The great cat of North American forests which we know as a lynx creeps quietly toward its prey, then swiftly closes in for the kill. Because certain members of the *Oxyopidae* family chase their intended victims in somewhat the same manner, the name "lynx spider" was suggested for them. Actually some species run swiftly through the foliage after insects, sometimes jumping from one branch to another, while others lie in wait near a flower and spring on the insects that come to visit it. While true lynxes prefer to hunt at night, their little spider namesakes hunt mostly by day.

A typical lynx spider is strongly built, with the body held well up on the legs. The eight legs, thin and fairly long, are equipped with black spines. Its bright eyes are set in four rows of two each, or are in two rows so curved that they practically form a circle. There is considerable variation in color. Some species are tinted bright green, but others are brownish gray. One found frequently in many parts of our country is the striped lynx. Its pale yellow body is covered with white scales, accented by four bands of dark scales. You must look carefully for this pretty creature, as it is not more than a third of an inch long.

More easily seen is the green lynx, which abounds in our southern states from coast to coast. Not only is it more brightly colored but it is larger—often three quarters of an inch in length. On the bright green body are rows of small red spots, and a red patch usually adorns the face. Also the legs are ringed with red at the joints.

38

Runners and Jumpers

Though the "lynx" and "wolf" and others may run and even pounce, there are two families set apart and known particularly as "jumping" spiders and "running" spiders. The jumpers (their family name is *Salticidae*) include many species, some of which are gaily ornamented, with scales and hairs of bright colors. They are noted for their keen eyesight, and one characteristic of the family is the arrangement of the eyes. There are four in the first row, two very small eyes in the second row, and two of medium size in a third row. They put this good vision to use by boldly hunting in bright daylight, usually stalking their prey slowly until a short distance away, then making a quick jump. They may even leap from a building to catch an insect in flight.

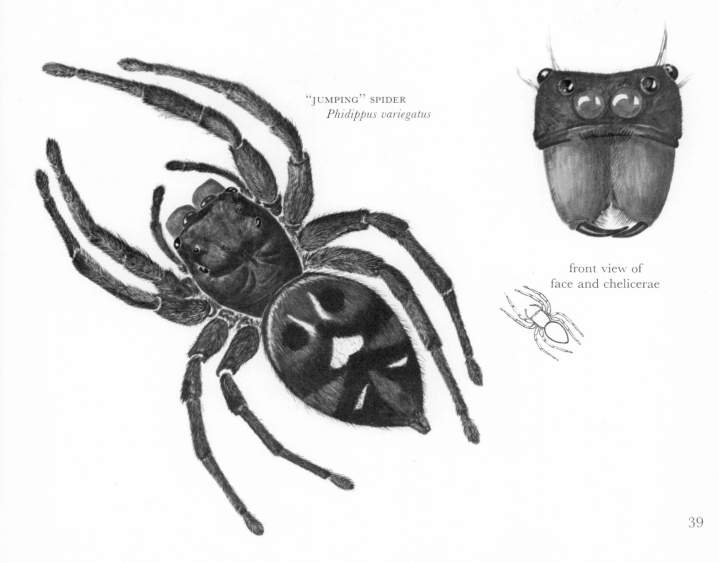

"JUMPING" SPIDER
Phidippus variegatus

front view of
face and chelicerae

39

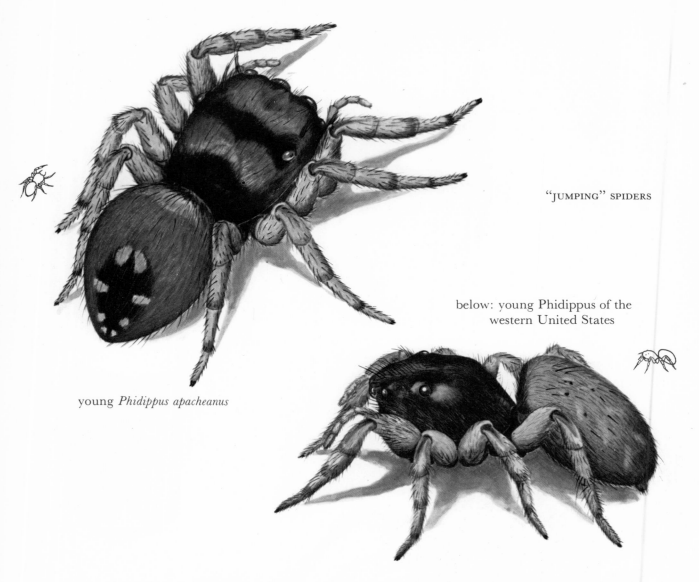

below: young Phidippus of the
western United States

young *Phidippus apacheanus*

In spite of its remarkable acrobatic ability, a jumping spider does not have especially long legs. They are of moderate length, and it is the first pair rather than the hind ones (with which jumps are accomplished) that are somewhat longer and thicker than the others.

Most of the jumping spiders are small, being a mere half inch or less in length. The largest American jumping spider is the gaily colored species *Phidippus*. An especially common member of this group *(Phidippus variegatus)* may be found running over tree trunks and under stones and logs. It ranges along the Atlantic coast west of the Rockies. Others thrive in all regions of our country. Among their interesting habits are the varied courtship dances performed by the males. In an effort to charm a mate, they carry on in quite an amazing fashion, some working up to a pitch of excitement that any jazz enthusiast might envy, others performing gracefully and quietly.

One type of jumping spider looks remarkably like ants—so much so that they are known as "antlike" spiders. They have quite slender bodies and thin, rather long legs. In some varieties white bands cross the body, giving it the appearance of being divided into several segments in the manner of an ant's body. In others, the body actually is constricted at one or more points, giving the impression of divisions. The antlike spiders are small, having roughly the same size and color as the ants they resemble. It is not unusual for them to walk and run in the fashion of ants, and even use the front legs as an ant uses its antennae.

Some running spiders shun the sunlight as much as the jumpers welcome it for hunting. They do not have the keen sight of their jumping relatives. Their activity in the daytime is mostly running from one shady spot to another; the search for food largely goes on at night. As a rule their coloring is dull—gray, brown, or black; however there are a few exceptions. One species is bright orange and black, adorned with white or colored stripes and spots. Another, extremely rare, has a pink body.

Not only do some of the running spiders mimic ants, as the jumpers do, they associate with the insects and may even move in with them! Apparently one of these spiders often constructs a little silken cell within an ant nest and lives there in fine style, feeding on the ant pupae and other small insects.

41

"RUNNING" SPIDER, *Poecilochroa variegata*

"JUMPING" SPIDER, *Phidippus apifex*

This CRAB SPIDER, *Misumena vatia*, has just moved on to a yellow flower and in a short time will take on the tone of the petals.

Crab Spiders

The short, broad form of its body, plus a crablike arrangement of the legs, would be sufficient reason to suggest the popular name of the crab spider. But besides these factors the little creatures walk sidewise and backward, crab-fashion, more readily then they move forward.

The "crabs" are true wanderers. Never involved in web spinning, nor in building retreats or nests for hibernating (except during the egg-laying period) they run about in pursuit of prey or lie in wait for some to come along. Some, which choose to conceal themselves in flowers, are brightly colored to match such a background. They are even able to change color from white to yellow, creating a better blend with their nesting place. Many spend their time along fences or on rocks and plants, in the winter hiding in cracks and under stones and bark. These are usually marked with gray and brown, making the spiders unnoticeable against the bark.

Though many crab spiders are small, one type—the huntsman spider of a related family—attains a body length of more than an inch and leg span of three or more inches. It is most common in tropical regions throughout the world but in America may be found as far north as Florida, Texas, and California. In the tropics it is looked upon as a house spider because it so often chooses to live in buildings, and frequently it is a welcome guest because it keeps in check such disagreeable insects as roaches. The huntsman has still another popular name, the banana spider, bestowed because many times it is carried into northern regions as a stowaway in a bunch of bananas. The tawny body blends well with the color of the ripened fruit.

Funnel-Web Builders

As we have seen, there are some spiders which build webs and are considered trappers, while others are out-and-out hunters. Here is the family *Agelenidae,* which does not belong completely to either group. Its numbers are equipped to be good hunters, with strong bodies and powerful jaws; nevertheless they spin large traps and their hunting activity is largely limited to running out over the spun silk to seize their prey. The popular name for *Agelenidae,* is "funnel-web" spider, for its typical web actually is a funnel shape, the outer opening spread like a field of white webbing over the grass, the lower opening contracted to a small tube. Usually the spider works at one web all its life and gradually a large, thick blanket is stretched out. Such

43

GRASS SPIDER, *Agelenopsis pennsylvanica*
(see page 19 for web)

sheets have sometimes been used in place of canvas by artists, although insect silk is more often employed for this type of art. Some paintings done on spider silk as long as a hundred years ago still survive.

Among the most commonly seen of the agelenids are the grass spiders. Their webs (some of them three feet across) are strewn far and wide in open fields and among the stones of roadside fences over areas from New England to Florida and from the east coast to Texas and Kansas. The spider is dark and quite large; the females often attain a body length of an inch. Despite the name grass spider, given because the webs are the most common ones found on grass, this weaver often makes its web in the angles of buildings and on plants at a considerable distance above the grass. In these cases the typical form of the funnel web is considerably changed. Grass spiders live only one year. In the fall a female leaves the web she has so diligently built, lays eggs and carefully hides away one or more egg sac in some protected spot. Soon afterward she dies. You may find the egg sacs beneath loose bark on trees and stumps during the winter. The spiderlings emerge in the spring, and in April and May the delicate new webs of the rising generation may be seen.

44

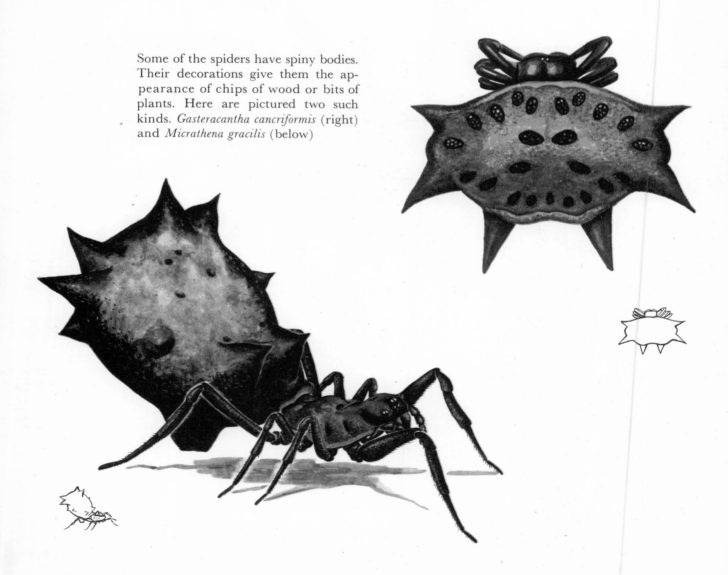

Some of the spiders have spiny bodies. Their decorations give them the appearance of chips of wood or bits of plants. Here are pictured two such kinds. *Gasteracantha cancriformis* (right) and *Micrathena gracilis* (below)

Sheet Weavers

Web of FILMY DOME SPIDER, *Linyphia marginata*. The dome is about three to five inches across.

With the group called "sheet weavers" we come to the spiders which fashion their entire lives around silk and so are a definite contrast to the prowling hunters. Though some are agile and run nearly as well as hunting spiders, all of them produce aerial webs which they rarely leave. Because their sight is less keen, they depend upon the creatures that fall into their silken traps. It is this fact rather than their location in relation to the earth that distinguishes the "aerial" web spinners from the hunters. For example, members of one family of sheet weavers not only live on the ground but in caves; yet, since they depend on trapping in the large sheets they spin on cave walls, they are considered part of the aerial group.

There are many varieties of sheet weavers. Their general plan of web construction is described on page 19 but let us see a few individual styles. The "bowl and doily" spider, found in almost every part of the United States, fashions one sheet like a shallow bowl. Above this it spins a web designed to knock down insects; below is a horizontal "doily." The spider then spends its time hanging between bowl and doily, waiting for victims. Another common sheet weaver is *Marginata,* whose delicate snares are often seen along streams or paths in moist woods. Both these spiders are small, measuring about one fifth of an inch in length.

45

Erigone is another sheet weaver that frequents the edges of streams and lakesides. Its two-inch-square webs may be found among grass roots or suspended from one stem to another over the water. So small are the erigonids—some no more than one twentieth of an inch long—it is not easy to see them, let alone examine them. Yet for the close observer there are a number of amazing features to be discovered. Some have a slender horn extending from between the eyes; on some, one pair of eyes is raised above the others on a rounded lobe. A European variety has a slender tower, more than twice the height of the head itself, as a built-in lookout post. Its eyes, in two groups, are located at the top and middle of the tower! Mostly *Erigone* is dark brown or black, but some species are light in color.

Certain close relatives of these spiders with the complicated eyes are cave spiders —which have lost all trace of eyes. Not all cave dwellers are totally blind, but at least their eyes tend to be smaller in size and sometimes fewer in number than their outdoor-living cousins.

In a roundabout way we may meet an occasional cave spider in our own houses, or in a barn. This darkly marked little weaver could be a descendant of cave dwellers which were brought to the United States from Europe, and which choose to settle in and around human habitations. However such is not the kind which truly deserves the title "domestic" or "house" spider.

The tiny *Erigone autumnalis* reveals its lovely color only when greatly magnified. The arrow points to the actual size of the spiders.

46

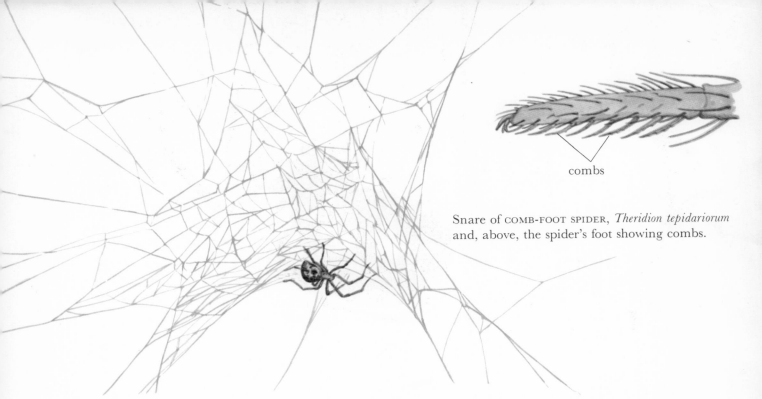

combs

Snare of COMB-FOOT SPIDER, *Theridion tepidariorum* and, above, the spider's foot showing combs.

House Spiders, and Other "Comb-Foots"

With the little creatures that most commonly weave tangled masses of silk in neglected rooms, we meet a group known as the "comb-footed" spiders. The family name is *Theridiidae*. Although it is a large family composed of many varying relatives, all members have the characteristic "comb"—a row of strong, curved bristles on the hind pair of legs. This is used for flinging silk (often in a rather liquid state) over prey that becomes entangled in the web.

You will find something about the irregular webs constructed by the theridiids on page 18. With the variety that exists in the family there naturally are variations in their webs, and while certain species live in houses and other protected places, others live on plants in the fields—their threads stretching here and there, and crossing in all directions. An interesting home made by one outdoor type is composed of bits of plants (often dried spruce needles) sewed together with silk, forming a strong waterproof tent. Most theridiids are small. Some, such as the common house spider, are of drab appearance, but others are brightly colored. Not only do theridiids live in dark places but they are active chiefly at night; as a result, sight is not of great importance to them. Their little eyes are grouped together at the front of the head.

Tiny as the theridiids are, their engineering skill gives them quite remarkable powers. With a well-organized series of steps, letting down threads and wrapping them about a victim, then tightening them, one of these spiders can hoist the victim from the ground up to its web. The common house spider, *Theridion tepidariorum,* may lift such creatures as small snakes and mice in this fashion.

47

BLACK WIDOW SPIDERS, *Latrodectus mactans*
above: female guarding egg sac
right: the male

Black Widows

For many people it may be difficult to think of the black widow as just another comb-footed spider (as it actually is), for its reputation as a deadly foe of mankind has overshadowed all facts known about it. As is mentioned in our first chapter, the poison of a black widow is rarely fatal to humans and the little creatures are not at all aggressive. Its popular name, which probably helps to build up its sinister reputation, is based on the fact that *sometimes* the female kills her mate; but this is a practice carried on by other species besides *Latrodectus mactans*—the "widow's" scientific name. Sometimes it is called the "hourglass" spider because of a red hourglass-shaped mark on its abdomen; again it is known as the "shoe-button" spider because of the form of its jet-black abdomen.

48

By any of these names, this spider is a spinner of tangled webs, making a rather small snare of coarse silk. Usually the webs are located close to the ground but may be well above it; always, however, they are in a dark location. One may be fitted into the deserted burrow of some little animal such as a field mouse, under stones or boards on the ground, or entwined in a grape arbor. Occasionally black widows seek a web-building spot inside a house, but they are not often found indoors. The spider often spends daylight hours in the silken tunnel that forms the core of the web.

The black widow has two very close relatives in our country. The "red-legged" widow of southern Florida, with legs reddish or banded with black and yellow, is one. Its poison is believed almost as harmful to humans as its better-known cousin. The other may be considered a brown or gray widow, since its color usually is grayish or light brown. Rarely it is jet black. It is found in Florida, but is most numerous in more tropical countries over much of the world.

49

BLACK WIDOW swathing
a grasshopper in silk

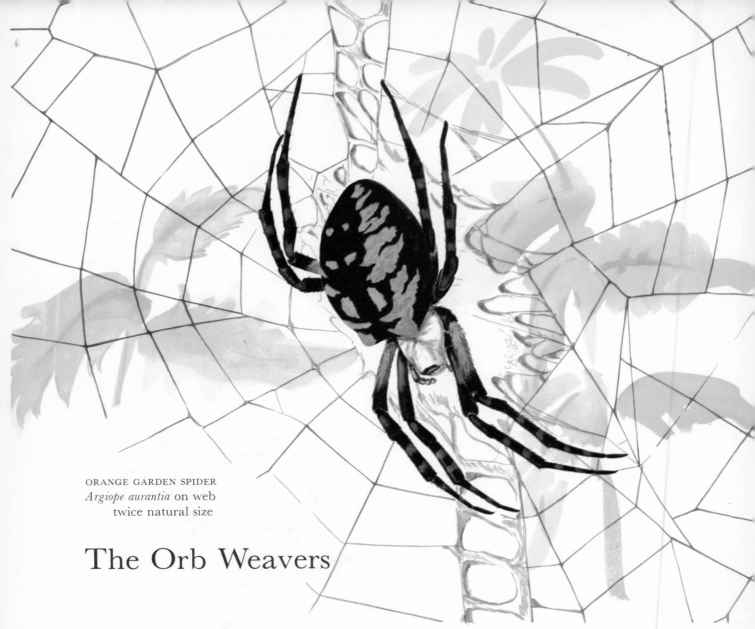

ORANGE GARDEN SPIDER
Argiope aurantia on web
twice natural size

The Orb Weavers

Weavers of that most wondrous of all kinds of webs—the orb—are remarkably numerous, not only in individuals but in various types. Giant of the lot is the tropical-living *Nephila*. A female, with a body perhaps more than two inches long and leg span of eight inches, may construct a golden silk orb at least three feet in diameter. The *Nephila* inhabiting our own country is somewhat smaller.

While the *Nephila* are largely confined to the far south, another orb weaver, the *Argiope,* is found far and wide throughout North America. The *Argiopes* flourish, too, in South America as well as in the Orient and Australia where they originated. One of the most generally known of the argiopes, in fact of all our spiders, is *Argiope aurantia,* the orange "garden" spider. The female is especially conspicuous, with her inch-long body brightly colored with orange or bright yellow spots on black. After building a large web, perhaps two feet in diameter, in a garden, meadow, or along a roadside, she remains at its center for much of the time waiting for grasshoppers and other insects to be ensnared. Even hot sunshine does not drive her to a shaded retreat.

Web of a RAY SPIDER, *Theridiosoma radiosa*, remarkable
for the fact that it has no hub. The radii come
together in a few lines, or rays, radiating
from the center. The entire structure is
known as a ray-formed web.
(see page 24 for egg sac)

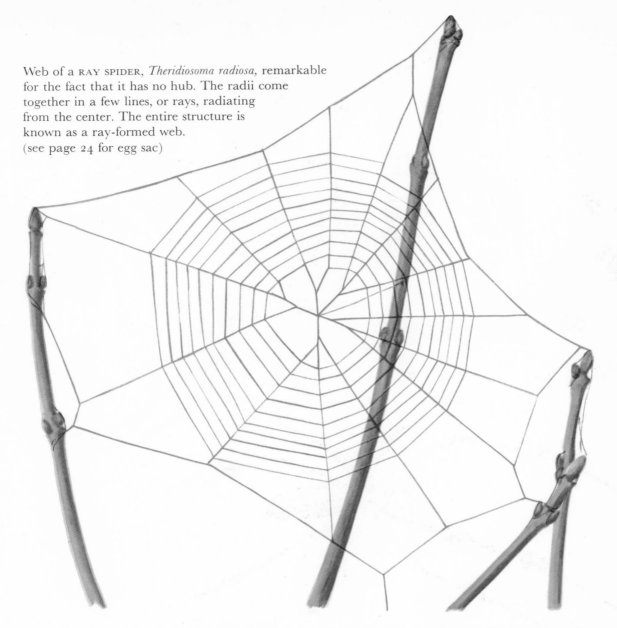

In the fall and early spring her pear-shaped egg sacs frequently may be seen hanging
from shrubs.

In our southern states is the related silver *argiope,* which takes this name from
its coloring of metallic silver and yellow. The banded *argiope* also is silvery white or
yellowish but is crossed by narrow darker lines.

Another notable orb-weaver is *Theridiosoma*. This kind of spider is very small
—a female usually measures no more than one tenth of an inch in length. Because
of the interesting use it makes of rays in its webs, it is often called the ray spider. As
its web is constructed, the radii do not all come together on one center as they do in
the usual orb. Instead they are united in groups of three or four, then each group is
connected with the center by a single thread. The web is actually drawn into the
shape of a cone by a thread which extends from the center to a nearby twig. The little
spider holds this thread tightly, but releases it suddenly when an insect touches the

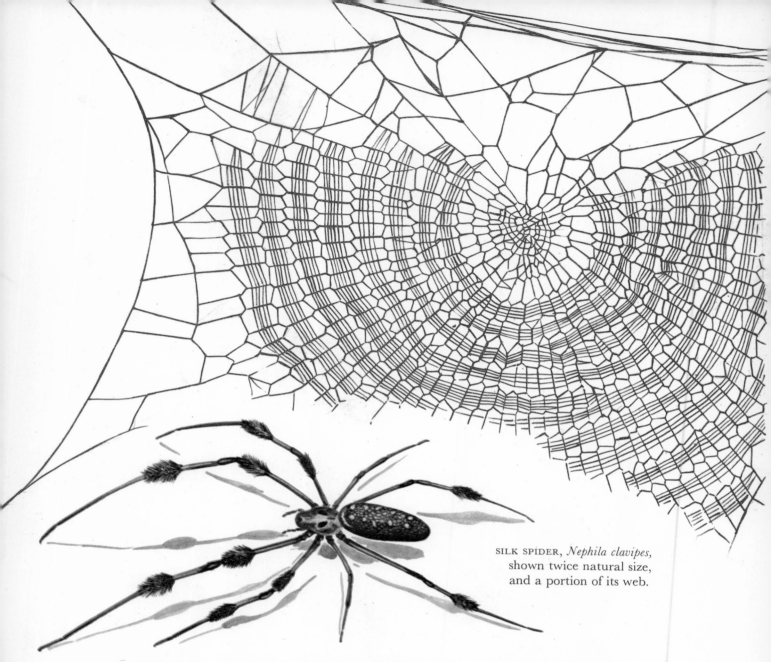

SILK SPIDER, *Nephila clavipes*,
shown twice natural size,
and a portion of its web.

web. This helps to ensnare the victim quickly. Ray spiders are most common in damp, dark locations, and their range extends from New England to Florida, west to the Mississippi.

The group know as "spiny-bodied" spiders take this name from the spines that ornament the abdomen of the females. When one of them hangs from the center of its orb web it looks more like a chip of wood or bit of a leaf than it does like an animal. In the tropics there are many bizarre types of spiny spiders, and several kinds live in our own country.

With the wide variety that exists in the appearance of the orb-weaving spiders, we find a number of differences in the details of the web: Some have bands of silk above or below the center, or both; some are without bands, some make a complete orb, others leave out certain spiral lines and radii and thus have an incomplete orb.

In Your Own Back Yard

From ancient times to the present, spiders have been featured in many a story, many a fable. We have seen how a Greek legend is connected with their scientific name. American Indians built countless tales around them, and some tribes regard them and their spinning as symbols. To one the orb web represents the heavens, with the mystery and power of the Great Spirit coming from its spirals. Another tribe credits the spider with being the first living creature on earth. Furthermore, the story goes, this spider had in its possession two small packages, and also had the power of magic song. By its singing the spider created from one package a woman who was ancestor to all Indians and from the other an ancestor for all other races. In more recent times we find the legend of Robert Bruce, discouraged in his efforts to win in-

The BANDED GARDEN SPIDER, *Argiope trifasciata*, which attaches its orb-shaped web to many familiar plants.

HUMPED ORB WEAVER, *Aranea gemmoides*

dependence for his native land, watching the untiring efforts of a spider to reach its home. From the little creature's patience he gained new determination to carry on his own fight.

But although the spiders found in story and history books are of great interest, still more fascinating are the spiders we can watch in our gardens, in fields and woodlands and in city parks. There are so many discoveries to be made about the life of a spider: We find that they, too, have their enemies. Frogs, toads and birds all devour them; a preying mantis will pounce on a spider of almost any size and eat it before it has a chance to fight back. Even the spiders that seem protected from such dangers because they tunnel into the ground are not always safe. We might sometime see a strange battle take place between the trap-door spider and its mortal enemy, the spider wasp. The fight is not of the spider's making. The wasp forces open the trap door to invade the burrow, attacks the eight-legged inmate, and before long usually

54

Three kinds of spiders often found in back yards and gardens.

below: *Aranea marmoreus*, and to the right, *Aranea trifolium*, both common throughout the United States.

lower right: one of the crab spiders, *Misumena vatia*, which can change its coloring from yellow to white to blend with its background. (see pages 6 and 42)

is successful in paralyzing its victim with a vicious sting. You might expect its next move would be to eat the spider, but this is not so. Instead it lays an egg on the spider's abdomen. When the larva hatches from this egg it proceeds to feed on its still-living but helpless host—and death is slow but certain for the spider. Yes, even those people who object to the trickster methods of the spider which persuades unsuspecting flies to "walk into my parlor," must admit its behavior is less gruesome than that of some of the enemies its fellow spiders encounter.

Altogether it does not take long for anyone who enjoys drama to be captivated by spiders. Theirs is a story of adventure and intrigue and of the development of amazing skills. As we watch them industriously spinning silk and constructing webs or fashioning underground homes, we cannot help but feel they truly earn their living. And the fact that their "living" consists of many unwanted insects should make us doubly anxious to welcome them as residents in our own neighborhoods.

55

Orb web of *Aranea marmoreus*

Index

Books for further reading about spiders:

AMERICAN SPIDERS by Willis J. Gertsch (D. Van Nostrand Co.)

HOW TO KNOW THE SPIDERS by B. J. Kaston (William C. Brown Co.)

THE LIFE OF THE SPIDER by John Crompton (Houghton Mifflin Co.)

THE SPIDER BOOK by John Henry Comstock (Doubleday, Doran Co.)

THE SPIDER'S WEB by Theodore H. Savory (Frederick Warne and Co.)